# THE FORTY-NINERS

by Daphne Greaves
illustrated by Cheryl Kirk Noll

**Harcourt**
SCHOOL PUBLISHERS

Cover, ©MPI/Getty Images; p.3, p.12, ©The Bancroft Library/Online Archives of California; p.4, ©Newberry Library/SuperStock; p.5, ©Anne Rippy/Iconica/Getty Images; p.6, ©C Squared Studios/ Photodisc Green/Getty Images; p.7, ©Library of Congress Prints & Photographs Division; p.8, p.9, ©Royalty-Free/Corbis; p.10, ©Jim West/Alamy; p.11, ©Chuck Pefley/Alamy; p.13, ©Digital Vision/Getty Images; p.14, ©Randy Mayor/PictureQuest.

Copyright © by Harcourt, Inc.

Requests for permission to make copies of any part of the work should be addressed to School Permissions and Copyrights, Harcourt, Inc., 6277 Sea Harbor Drive, Orlando, Florida 32887-6777. Fax: 407-345-2418.

HARCOURT and the Harcourt Logo are trademarks of Harcourt, Inc., registered in the United States of America and/or other jurisdictions.

Printed in China

ISBN 10: 0-15-350991-0
ISBN 13: 978-0-15-350991-9

Ordering Options
ISBN 10: 0-15-350601-6 (Grade 4 On-Level Collection)
ISBN 13: 978-0-15-350601-7 (Grade 4 On-Level Collection)
ISBN 10: 0-15-357944-7 (package of 5)
ISBN 13: 978-0-15-357944-8 (package of 5)

D0464396

2 3 4 5 6 7 8 9 10 985 12 11 10 09 08 07

## Characters

| | | | |
|---|---|---|---|
| Narrator 1 | Sarah | Ma | Jake |
| Narrator 2 | Pa | Marcus | |

**Setting:** The Oregon-California Trail

**Narrator 1:** There's gold in them there hills!

**Narrator 2:** This was the rumor that started the California gold rush.

**Narrator 1:** On January 24, 1848, a worker named James Marshall picked up a small, shiny object from a river on John Sutter's farm.

**Narrator 2:** Marshall turned the pea-sized object over in his hand. He held it up to the sunlight to better scrutinize it. "Gold!" he exclaimed.

**Narrator 1:** John Sutter swore Marshall to secrecy about his discovery. Sutter had plans to build a farming empire. He did not want prospectors to descend on California looking for gold and eroding the land.

**Narrator 2:** However, a secret like this was too colossal to keep. Soon word got out. By 1849, prospectors were heading to California from all over.

**Narrator 1:** They became known as the forty-niners. They were men and women dedicated to following their dream of riches.

**Narrator 2:** They endured hardship and danger in pursuit of what some called a foolish illusion.

**Narrator 1:** Like thousands of other men, women, and children, the Boyd family made their way west.

**Narrator 2:** Young Sarah Boyd kept a journal about the family's gold-seeking adventure.

**Sarah:** *May 9, 1849 – On the Oregon-California Trail – It seems hard to believe that only two weeks ago, we were all snug in our cabin. Then, like everyone else, Pa got gold fever. He came home one memorable day shouting.*

**Pa:** Gold! They've discovered gold in California, and I'm going to get us some!

**Sarah:** Ma didn't say a word. She just took out the trunk and began packing our things.

**Pa:** Mother, what do you think you're doing?

**Ma:** Where you go, I go.

**Sarah:** Pa was dubious about this idea she had of coming along.

**Pa:** Now, Mother, don't be foolish. What about the children?

**Sarah:** Ma still insisted.

**Ma:** What about them? Where I go, my children go.

**Sarah:** Marcus, my younger brother, began running frantically around the cabin.

**Marcus:** Gold! Gold! Gold!

**Sarah:** *June 10, 1849 Two weeks later, we had packed everything in the wagon and were heading to California. Pa says we're going to strike it rich. I think that might be nice. Whatever happens, this is the biggest adventure of my life!*

Gold nuggets

**Narrator 1:** Like other forty-niners, the Boyds faced months of travel to get to California.

**Narrator 2:** They would cross raging rivers and white hot deserts.

**Narrator 1:** There would be interesting sights along the way.

**Narrator 2:** There would also be hardship and long days of terrible boredom.

**Sarah:** *July 12, 1849 – On the Oregon-California Trail – Day after day, we go on and on. Every day is the same. At daybreak, we rise and yoke the oxen to the wagon. We travel all day, and at sunset, we make camp. The next day, we get up and do it all over again. The sight of travelers' belongings embedded in the dirt along the trail is common. Pots and pans, furniture, and contraptions of all kinds can be found. Today our family added something to the strange sights along the trail.*

**Ma:** I won't do it!

**Pa:** We have to. The oxen are tired. If we want to make it to California, we have to lighten our load.

**Ma:** Father, that dining room table belonged to my mother. It's the most distinguished thing I own!

**Pa:** I know, Mother, I know.

**Ma:** All right. Let's do it and get back on the trail.

**Sarah:** As I write these words, I can hear Ma crying.

**Marcus:** Sarah, what's the matter with Ma? Why is she crying?

**Sarah:** She's just a little sad.

**Pa:** You two go to sleep now and get a good rest. Tomorrow we'll be in the vicinity of the Forty Mile Desert.

**Narrator 1:** The Forty Mile Desert was a dry wasteland between the Humboldt and Carson Rivers in present-day Nevada. Thankfully, it was near the end of the journey.

**Narrator 2:** It may also have been the hardest part of the trip.

9

**Narrator 1:** Travelers who didn't bring enough water didn't make it across the desert.

**Narrator 2:** The Boyds had plenty of water. However, they soon faced another danger.

**Narrator 1:** Many forty-niners became sick because of unhealthy conditions while traveling.

**Narrator 2:** The roadside was dotted with the fresh graves of those forty-niners who did not survive the journey.

**Sarah:** *July 28, 1849 – The Forty Mile Desert – I am so scared. Marcus is sick. Yesterday I scolded him for walking too slowly.*

**Marcus:** I can't go any faster, Sarah. I'm tired, and I hurt.

**Sarah:** Abruptly, Marcus dropped to the ground.

**Ma:** Marcus! Oh, my goodness, Marcus!

**Sarah:** Pa scooped him up and put him in the wagon. Ma tried to wake him. He just moaned and wouldn't open his eyes.

**Marcus:** I'm so tired, Ma.

**Sarah:** *July 29, 1849 – The Forty Mile Desert – Pa says Marcus is very sick. Ma's trying to make him better. It's so quiet without Marcus running around. I wish he'd come over and ask me what I'm writing. I wish he'd nag me to play with him. I wish we'd never left home. I don't want to be rich! I just want Marcus.*

**Marcus:** Ma? I'm hungry . . .

**Ma:** Thank goodness! Thank goodness!

**Narrator 1:** The entire Boyd family made it to California.

**Narrator 2:** Soon they faced new obstacles.

**Sarah:** *December 12, 1849 – Sacramento, California – We have been in Sacramento for several weeks now. Pa says it is a city. I guess so. There are wooden buildings, and I have never seen so many people in my life. They rush everywhere. No one speaks without yelling. They all have gold fever. Things have not turned out the way we had hoped. Pa hasn't found much gold yet. I know he's worried. At night, I've heard him talking to Ma.*

**Pa:** I think I made a mistake coming out here.

**Ma:** Others have found gold. You will too.

**Pa:** There is gold here, but the time is past for making fortunes. It's getting harder to find. When you do find it, it's almost impossible to dig out of the rocks.

**Ma:** We'll be all right. I just know it.

**Sarah:** *February 4, 1850 – Sacramento, California – Ma is right; we are going to be all right. Pa still hasn't found any gold, but something else happened. A few weeks ago, Ma was cooking our dinner over the campfire. One of the prospectors came up to her. He said his name was Jake.*

**Jake:** Ma'am, I discern by my nose that you are a fine cook. I'll pay you for a biscuit.

**Ma:** I'm sorry, but this is for my family.

**Jake:** I'll give you six dollars.

**Ma:** What?

**Sarah:** Ma nearly fainted when Jake put a bag of gold dust in her hand.

**Jake:** I estimate that's worth six dollars, and I can verify that it's the real thing too.

### Bag of gold dust

**Sarah:** Ma gave Jake a biscuit, and he's been a steady customer ever since. Ma started cooking for many prospectors.

**Ma:** Hello, Jake. How are you and your friends tonight?

**Jake:** Hungry, ma'am, we're hungry.

**Pa:** Well, sit down. My wife is making beef stew tonight.

**Sarah:** *March 9, 1850 – Sacramento, California – Business is good; especially when one of the prospectors strikes gold. On those days, they eat and talk as long as Ma lets them stay. Business has been so good that Pa stopped prospecting. He's building a hotel with a restaurant. We're calling it "All That Glistens." Pa says we struck gold after all.*

# Think Critically

1. What was the name of the trail that the Boyd family traveled on to California?

2. The narrator said that finding gold in California was a colossal secret to keep. What does the word *colossal* on page 4 mean?

3. What did the forty-niners all have in common with one another?

4. Sarah wrote in her journal, "Pa says we struck gold after all." What did she mean?

5. Should Pa have traveled to California with his family? Explain your answer.

## Science

**Periodic Table** Gold is an element. Elements make up everything on Earth. Look up gold on the periodic table of the elements. Find its symbol and atomic number. Write them in the middle of a sheet of paper. Then write the names of some things that are made of gold.

 **School-Home Connection** Read this Readers' Theater with your family. Talk about the sacrifices these travelers had to make on their journey.

**Word Count:** 1,291 (1,297)